57-

D1134474

The
Absent-Minded Farmer

and

Other Stories for Children of all Ages

By

CYRIL H. JONES

Published by

B. McCALL BARBOUR
28 GEORGE IV BRIDGE
EDINBURGH, 1, SCOTLAND

MADE AND PRINTED IN GREAT BRITAIN BY
STANLEY L. HUNT (PRINTERS) LTD., GEORGE STREET, RUSHDEN, NORTHANTS

This book is dedicated to my wife Molly, and two boys, David and Andrew; also my parents-in-law, for their Christian love and influence; and to the sacred memory of my own dear parents.

CONTENTS

INTRODUCTION

WITHIN the following pages is a selection of stories for children of all ages, which can be used by parents as *Bed-time Stories*, or by ministers and lay preachers as *Children's Addresses*, or by Sunday School and Day School teachers to illustrate their lessons. Even "grown-ups", who are still young at heart, will find them enjoyable and spiritually profitable.

I would like to thank Mr. H. C. Smith, of the E.C.L. Book Shop, Bristol, for his help and kindness, not only concerning this book, but in many other ways.

CYRIL H. JONES.

THE ABSENT-MINDED FARMER

"Lo, I am with you alway, even unto the end of the world"
St. Matt. 28. 20

THIS particular farmer lived about fifteen miles from the city of Gloucester. He had a very bad memory, so whenever he went to town, he carried with him a slip of paper on which was written a list of calls to be made or articles to be obtained.

On one particular market day he went up to Gloucester with a few sheep in the car trailer, some eggs, and other farm produce. Having sold his sheep and the other articles for a good price, he pulled out his list to see what he now had to buy to take back to the farm. As he went round the various shops and made his purchases, he crossed off each item on his list, until his shopping was completed.

Then, happening to meet a farmer friend, they began discussing together how they had fared at the market—what they had sold, and the prices obtained. His friend mentioned that a cricket match was in progress, and asked him if he would like to watch it for an hour. Our absent-minded friend agreed; but after an hour or so of rather slow cricket, he decided he had better start for home.

First he checked his list to make sure that he had made all his purchases. Then he set off on the fifteen-mile drive home.

After travelling five miles he suddenly had a strange feeling that he had forgotten something. So he stopped, pulled out his list, checked every item in the car trailer, shook his head, decided he *had* everything, and started off again.

Another five miles sped by, but still he had an uneasy feeling that something was missing. So he stopped once more, double checked all the items on his list, and being

13

now thoroughly satisfied that he *did* have everything correct, he drove thoughtfully home.

Soon he entered the farmyard, and after unhitching the trailer and putting his car away, he gathered up some of his purchases and made his way towards the farmhouse. The back door of his home suddenly opened, and his little daughter ran out to greet him. "Have you had a good day, Daddy?" "Yes, my dear." "Daddy, where's Mummy?" MUMMY! Oh, dear! That's it! Mother was still in Gloucester. Father had not put her on his list, and through going to the cricket match had forgotten all about picking Mother up, after she had completed *her* shopping. Poor Father had to get the car out again, rush back into Gloucester, and explain to Mother, who was rather puzzled and impatient by now, just what had happened.

We may rest assured that Mother headed Father's list every time after that experience!

Would *you* forget *your* mother, or father, especially if away on holiday in a strange place? I doubt it. Usually boys and girls keep one or other, or both, in sight, and by so doing feel safe and secure.

After Jesus Christ ascended into Heaven, following His Resurrection, one can easily see that the disciples could have been forgiven for thinking that Jesus was leaving them for good. Left to themselves it would have been easy for Peter to say, "Well, I've been the leader and preacher until now, it's time John took over." Or perhaps John could have said, "No, I'm not going to preach, let James, or one of the others have a go." If they had spoken, and acted like that, then the Gospel of Jesus Christ would never have been preached, and the Christian Church would soon have come to a full stop. But Jesus had made His disciples a wonderful promise, " Lo, I am *with you* alway, even unto the end of the world," and they believed that promise as they went out obeying His command, "Go ye, therefore, and teach all nations ".

Never, for one minute, forget that Jesus is always with us, as our constant Companion, Friend and Saviour. Don't be like the absent-minded farmer who forgot the one who mattered most. You love your parents, and rightly so—love also, and follow, the One Who matters most in life—Jesus Christ!

> "Jesus, Friend of little children,
>   Be a friend to me;
> Take my hand, and ever keep me
>   Close to Thee.
>
> Never leave me, nor forsake me;
>   Ever be my Friend;
> For I need Thee, from life's dawning
>   To its end."

THE CHRISTIAN'S SECRET SIGN

"Follow Me, and I will make you fishers of men" St. Matt. 4. 19

BOYS and girls love wearing badges—sometimes the more the merrier! All sorts and shapes of badges—some that you obtain by collecting such things as jam labels, and others that have to be worked for, especially if you are a Scout, Girl Guide, or engaged in some form of useful service.

I know boys and girls who are proud to wear Christian Endeavour badges, Scripture Union badges, Boys' Brigade or Girls' Life Brigade badges, and such like, but not very many wear the badge with the sign of the fish stamped on it. The Sign of the Fish? What has that got to do with being a Christian?

Well now, our text above tells us of the words of Jesus to His fishermen friends, "Follow Me, and I will make you fishers of men". Peter, Andrew, James and John understood all about fish, and how to catch them. Jesus taught them how to understand people, and how to "catch" them for the service of Jesus.

As the years went by, during the early Church period, Christians were persecuted for their faith, and it became

15

dangerous to let everyone know that they were Christians. So they adopted a secret sign—the Sign of the Fish.

Imagine now two travellers approaching each other along a lonely and dusty road. Both stop and greet each other, and ask about the town from which each has come. One man uses his staff to draw something in the dust. The other looks down and sees the outline of a fish. Eagerly he says, "Are you a Christian?" "Yes," is the reply. Now both men greet each other as brothers in Christ, and speak of their work for the Master. But how did they know? What did the sign of the fish stand for?

The word "fish" in Greek was "ichthus", and by splitting this word up into I CH TH U S, Christians were able to make an anagram of our Master's titles: "Jesus Christ, God's Son, Saviour". In these few words you have a true statement of our Christian faith.

Do you know why more fish are sold on a Friday than on any other day of the week, and why more fish are sold on Good Friday than on any other day of the year? I have even conducted services on Good Friday morning with people in Church complete with their purchases of fish. We put up with the smell! But I doubt very much if even these good people knew *why* they observed the age-old custom of buying fish on a Good Friday.

In our anagram we read, "Jesus Christ, God's Son, SAVIOUR". There we have the secret. On Good Friday Jesus became our Saviour. As the hymn-writer puts it, clearly and simply:

> "There is a green hill far away,
>   Without a city wall,
> Where the dear Lord was crucified,
>   Who died to save us all."

Jesus wants you to become a fisher of men for Him, and one way to witness is to reveal the "secret sign" to boys and girls at school. Draw a fish either on a piece of paper, or in the dust on the playground, and ask your friends if they know what it is, and what it stands for. They will probably be able to tell you what it is, but only you will be able to tell them what the sign stands for, and

16

what it means to Christian boys and girls and grown-ups. Remember the message of the sign, your "five finger exercise"—"Jesus Christ, God's Son, Saviour".

May you become good fishers of men for Jesus Christ.

TRAFFIC LIGHTS

"When he came to himself . . . I will arise and go . . . and he arose, and came to his father" St. Luke 15. 17-20

WHAT are the three colours on Traffic Lights? From the top down we have Red, Amber and Green. Red means STOP. Amber means CONSIDER or GET READY; and Green means Go.

A group of children were playing a rather dangerous game which involved running across a main road. One child got half way across, slipped on the proverbial banana skin, and fell. At that moment a motor car, speeding along the road, was unable to pull up until right over the boy. Fortunately it was a high car, and the bodywork and wheels missed him completely. The little chap crawled from underneath, was picked up by a lady living nearby, and carried home screaming his head off. Apart from a good shaking up he was none the worse.

That boy was myself! Now, whenever I am about to cross a road, I stop at the kerb; consider if the way is clear to my right and then to my left; look right again and, if the road is clear, I go across without delay.

You all know, or ought to know, the Highway Code Rules for STOPPING, CONSIDERING AND GOING. But do you know similar rules for the Highway Code of Life? Did you know that "Traffic Lights" are mentioned in the New Testament, in a Parable which Jesus told? It is called the parable of the Prodigal Son.

A younger son became rather "fed up" with life at home, and wanted to have his own "fling". So he asked his father to give him his share of the estate. His father

17

granted him his request, whereupon the disgruntled young man packed his bag and left home for the "bright lights" of the city. There, as long as his money lasted, he found plenty of friends of a kind. But, when the money vanished, so did the "friends". Being penniless now, he had to look for a job, and the only one available was that of looking after pigs. Now the young man was a Jew, and for a Jew to work amongst swine was terrible, because Jews regard the pig as an unclean animal. It happened at this time that there was a famine in the land and food was scarce, so much so that no one would give the young run-away anything to eat, and he became so hungry that he would almost have eaten the food for the swine. Added to his hunger was the fact that he was now very sorry for himself. He thought of the well-paid and well-fed servants employed by his father. So he STOPPED what he was doing, and said, "How many hired servants of my father's have bread enough and to spare, and I perish with hunger." So he CONSIDERED, "I will arise and go to my father, and will say unto him, 'Father, I have sinned against heaven, and before thee, and am no more worthy to be called thy son: make me as one of thy hired servants'."

So he arose to GO to his father.

You all know how the father saw his son afar off, and went running to greet him, putting his arms round him, and giving him a kiss, and how the son started to say how sorry he was to have hurt his father through his wrong doing, and now he begged his father's forgiveness, and said that he was no longer worthy to be called his son.

But the father wouldn't hear of it but instead gave orders for his servants to bring fresh clothing (including the best robe) to replace the rags on his back; new shoes for his feet; a ring for his finger as a sign that he was not only forgiven, but also restored again as a full son in the family of his father.

When we say and do things that are wrong, then the RED light comes up to warn us of danger—our conscience tells us that we are sinning. It is then high time for us to

CONSIDER just what we are doing, or have done, and to repent of our ways, and be sorry before God and those whom we have wronged. We should then immediately Go to God, seeking His forgiveness through His Son Jesus Christ, and afterward Go to the person we have hurt or wronged and ask their forgiveness.

Remember the words of the Lord's Prayer, which you pray every day: "FORGIVE US . . . AS WE FORGIVE THEM THAT TRESPASS (or sin) AGAINST US."

Remember also the words of the hymn—the "Safety First" hymn:

> "Yield not to temptation,
> For yielding is sin;
> Each victory will help you
> Some other to win.
> Fight manfully onward,
> Dark passions subdue;
> LOOK EVER TO JESUS,
> He will carry you through."

THE JOY SONG
AND I'M THIRD

"That your joy might be full" St. John 15. 11

A MINISTER in London had been invited to preside over a young people's annual meeting at a neighbouring church. It was his first visit there, so he left home in good time, through pouring rain. He was the first to arrive there, and discovered that the meeting was to be held in an upper room. Looking around the room he spotted several texts, some certificates, and photographs of Sunday School teachers who, judging by their dress, had lived long, long ago. Side whiskers and beards helped to complete the picture!

Looking back towards the door, he saw a clock, and over the clock a motto with these words: "I'M THIRD". He thought—"'I'm Third'. There's the caretaker and myself, but we only make two. It can't be that." Turning to the caretaker, who was doing some last minute dusting, the minister said, "Can you tell me what those words mean, please?" The caretaker had a look at the clock and, shaking his head, he replied, "I've read those words a hundred times, and I've dusted them now and again, but I don't know what they mean." After a while he had a flash of inspiration, "I think my daughter Sylvia knows." Off he went downstairs, and meanwhile the minister continued his tour of inspection of the ancient photographs.

Shortly, the caretaker returned, puffing away. "Sylvia says, 'the words mean what they say—I'm Third'." "I see," said the minister, though none the wiser. Then the caretaker went on, "It's the motto of the young people —Jesus first; Others second; and I'm Third." "Why, of course," said the minister.

Just then the door opened, and in trooped the young people, undaunted by the pouring rain outside. Soon the meeting was under way, and the minister was amazed to discover the great amount of work put in during the previous year. Not only had meetings been well attended, but young people had taken an interest in old people, sick people and blind folk, running their errands, digging their gardens and so on. The minister thought, "Yes, there is the 'I'm Third' note!" They sang about it in the words of the hymn:

"Be not selfish in your greed. Pass it on!
Look upon another's need. Pass it on!"

Like all good things, even this meeting had to come to a close. One girl dashed downstairs, and came back to say that it was still pouring with rain. "You take my mac, Doris. I haven't far to go." The minister thought, "There it is again—'I'm Third'."

When he reached home, and shared his experiences with his wife, he said to her, "What a different place the world would be if everyone in it adopted 'I'm Third' as their motto for life—instead of putting self first, putting

Jesus first, then others in the world second, and ourselves last of all."

If you boys and girls would know the meaning of real Christian Joy, then take that word "Joy" and divide it up into J-O-Y, and sing and live out each day the J-O-Y SONG:

> "Jesus and Others and You,
> What a wonderful way to spell Joy!
> Jesus and Others and You
> In the heart of each girl and boy!
> J is for Jesus, for He has first place;
> O is for Others, of many a race;
> Y is for you, and whatever you do
> Put yourself in the *very last* place!"

ST. MARTIN AND THE BEGGAR

"Inasmuch as ye have done it unto one of the least of these My brethren, ye have done it unto Me" St. Matt. 25. 40

IF ever you visit the parish of St. Martin in the Fields in London, you will notice on all the lamp posts in the parish a medallion bearing a picture of St. Martin dividing his cloak with a beggar.

Martin was born in Austria many hundreds of years ago, and one of the stories told about this Christian man is shown on the medallions in the parish in London named after him.

On a severe winter's day, a poor old man stood by the wayside begging, and shivering in the cold. A young soldier came along that way, but the old man did not expect any help or sympathy from him. That soldier's name was Martin who, on seeing the old man, felt so sorry for him that he actually drew his sword, cut his soldier's cloak in two and gave one half to the beggar.

Some of the passers-by laughed at Martin for doing what they thought was a stupid thing. That night, however, Martin had a dream in which he saw Jesus

Christ, and He was actually wearing the half cloak which he had given to the beggar.

Martin eventually gave up being a soldier, and devoted the rest of his life to the work of sharing his religion as he had shared his cloak. He later became a bishop, and made missionary tours which won him the title of "The Apostle of Gaul". The story of his life is a record of one who was a faithful soldier and servant of the Lord Jesus Christ to his life's end.

It is very appropriate that the church in London which bears his name, St. Martin in the Fields, should care for poor and homeless and needy people. Thousands and thousands of men and women have been fed and given shelter in that church.

Remember the words of Jesus whenever the opportunity arises for you to do a kindness to someone in need—"Inasmuch as ye have done it unto one of the least of these My brethren, ye have done it unto Me".

THE GRASSHOPPER
THAT SAVED A BOY'S LIFE

"And the grasshopper" Ecclesiastes 12. 5

ONE summer's day, a young boy, on his way home from school along a country lane, enjoyed himself chasing the birds and the butterflies, until he startled a grasshopper. He then began chasing it, and my, how that grasshopper could jump! To escape the boy, it at last jumped over a fence, whereupon the boy followed. But that was as far as the chase went for there, on the ground on the other side of the fence, lay a bundle of clothes, cosily covering the form of a baby boy, whose sweet, innocent face and lovely eyes at once attracted him. Seeing no one around, and feeling that it was unsafe to leave the little one lying there, he decided that the best thing to do was to take it home to his mother. Having come to this decision, he gathered the little bundle into his arms and made for home.

The little unwanted baby was nameless. No one ever knew who was its mother or where it had come from. And so this little baby boy was taken into this new home and cared for as a member of the family.

You might not expect much from a boy who had received such a strange start in life, and yet this boy grew up to be a remarkably clever man, and, what is more important still, an exceedingly good man. He became rich and powerful, and served his country so well that he was knighted, and is known in history by the honourable name of Sir Thomas Gresham.

In the heart of the city of London there is an imposing building called the Royal Exchange. It was built in honour of Sir Thomas Gresham; and at the top of this building you will see, not a rooster nor a cross, but a grasshopper. That grasshopper still tells the story of how a grasshopper was used by God to guide the footsteps of a little schoolboy in the rescue of a little abandoned child.

There is a story in the Bible about a little baby boy who was found in a basket by the riverside. A princess found him, adopted him as her own, and had him brought up in the palace in all the wealth and culture of Egypt. No one, apart from God, ever knew that Moses was destined to become a prince in Egypt, and later on the greatest leader and law-giver this world has ever known.

God has a wonderful way of caring for little children. And God loves and cares for you. God needs you and perhaps has some wonderful work for you to do which no one can do but you. And one day if you keep close to Him, God will make that work plain and clear to you.

MARY JONES AND HER BIBLE

"And a little child shall lead them" Isaiah 11. 6

MARY JONES lived with her father and mother in a little Welsh village called Llanfihangel. Above the village towered the craggy summit of Cader Idris. Mary's parents were poor. Her father was a weaver, and from early morning till late at night he worked hard. It was pleasant work, but was poorly paid, and luxuries were unknown in Mary's home.

There was one night in the week to which Mary always looked forward. It was the night when people gathered from far and near to listen to stories read from a Welsh Bible. Coming home from the meeting one night, Mary said, "Mother, why can't we have a Bible of our own?" "Bibles are scarce, child," said her mother, "and very costly."

A few days later a neighbour, Mrs. Evans, called at Mary's home, and Mrs. Jones told her how she was concerned about Mary and her schooling. Mary looked up. "Oh," she said, "if only I could learn to read, I should like to read the Bible stories." Mrs. Evans said, "Perhaps some day you will get your chance to learn. When that day comes you are welcome to come and read my Bible as often as you like." "Oh, thank you," said Mary, "that is kind of you. It is only two miles up to your place."

Weeks and months went by. Then Mary's father came home one day with the news that a school was to open in a village two miles away. Mary danced round the little kitchen. "Now," she said, "I shall learn to read!"

At long last the happy day came when Mary could read, and she went as often as possible to Mrs. Evans' house to read God's Word. But, she longed to have a Bible of her own.

She started doing jobs for the neighbours. Then Mrs. Evans gave her two hens, and Mary sold the eggs. For six whole years she saved, until at last she had enough money to buy a Bible of her very own.

But where was such a Bible to be obtained? There

were no shops that sold Bibles. Her schoolmaster told her of a minister, Rev. Thomas Charles of Bala, twenty-five miles away, who sometimes could get Bibles for people. That was all the information Mary required. After obtaining her parents' permission to undertake the journey of twenty-five miles on foot, Mary set off early one morning, carrying her little money-box, her lunch and her shoes—for she feared they might get dusty if she wore them.

All that day she walked on and on. It was almost dark when she reached Bala, her journey's end. That night Mary sought out the home of a good friend, and in the morning they both went to see Mr. Charles. It was still dark when they reached his house, and when Mr. Charles came to the door, he was surprised to see anyone so early. Mary, however, soon told him her story.

Mr. Charles had only one Bible left, and that had been half-promised to someone. Mary was moved to tears when she heard this disappointing news. Suddenly Mr. Charles rose from his chair and laid his hand on Mary's head. "My child," he said, "you *shall* have your Bible. I cannot send you away empty, no matter who else goes short."

Half an hour later Mary was on her way home again, her heart so full of happiness that she actually forgot to count the miles. And late that night she came to her own little home under the mountains. Before going to bed that night, Mary read, with a thrill in her voice, the 150th Psalm. "Praise ye the Lord. Praise God in His sanctuary; praise Him in the firmament of His power." And when she came to the last verse—"Let everything that hath breath praise the Lord; praise ye the Lord," her voice rose in triumph.

Rising from their seats with one accord, the family knelt together and gave thanks to God.

Two years later the Rev. Thomas Charles went to London, and told some of his friends there of little Mary Jones and her long, long walk to Bala to buy a Bible. "What a pity it is," they said, "that this Book is so hard

25

to get. Let us start a society to print Bibles and make them cheap so that even the poorest child can have one; and let us print so many that they can be had without having to go so long a journey for one."

That was the start of the British and Foreign Bible Society which has gone on printing Bibles ever since.

THE CHURCH OF THE VOW

"And Jacob vowed a vow, saying, 'If God will be with me, and will keep me in this way that I go . . . this stone, which I have set for a pillar, shall be God's House' " Genesis 28. 20-22

IN the year 1773, during the reign of George III, a young man, twenty-one years of age, named John Hare, left Crowcombe at the foot of the Quantock Hills, to seek his fortune in the city of Bristol. He arrived on the outskirts very early one morning before daybreak, and instead of going into the city at that hour, he slept in an orchard.

He had a delightful dream, and when he awoke and found himself in a beautiful orchard with the birds singing and the heavens smiling—for it was the month of May— he vowed a vow that, if God spared his life, and prospered him, he would build a House of God on that very spot.

As the years went by John Hare prospered, and the solemn vow made to God was never forgotten. On June 1st, 1830, the new church was finally completed, and on June 15th it was opened for divine worship, the sermon being preached by the famous Dr. Thomas Chalmers of Scotland.

It is one thing to make a vow (or promise), and quite another thing to keep it. As you grow older, and understand more and more what the promises of God mean to His children—for God keeps His promises—how thankful you will come to be that, early in life, you were taught to *keep* your vows and promises.

Jacob made a vow, and that vow was the turning point in his life. John Hare made a vow, and that vow was the turning point in *his* life. When *you* make a solemn vow to God, and surrender the whole of your life to Him, through Jesus Christ, His Son and our Saviour, *that* will be the turning point in *your* life.

Do it to-day—DO IT NOW!

DISCIPLES AND APOSTLES

"And when He had called unto Him His twelve disciples . . .
Now the names of the twelve apostles are these . . ." St. Matt.
10. 1 and 2

DO you know the difference between a disciple and an apostle? That's rather a hard question—one that even the grown-ups would find difficult to answer.

Before I give you the answer, let me pass on to you some verses describing what three boys at any rate would like to be when they grow up:

> "When I'm a man, a man,
> I'll be a carpenter, if I can—and I can!
> I'll plane like this, and I'll hammer so,
> And this is the way my saw shall go.
> I'll make bird-houses, and sleds and boats,
> And a ship that shall race every craft that floats,
> When I'm a man.
>
> When I'm a man, a man,
> A doctor I'll be, if I can—and I can!
> My powders and pills shall be nice and sweet,
> And you shall have just what you like to eat;
> I'll prescribe for you riding, and sailing, and such;
> And, 'bove all things, you must never study too much,
> When I'm a man.
>
> When I'm a man, a man,
> I'll be a minister, if I can—and I can!
> And once in a while a sermon I'll make
> That will keep little boys and girls awake;
> For—ah, dear me, if the ministers knew
> How glad we are when they get through—
> When I'm a man."

A few years ago I took my driving test (I took it twice!), and at long last I was able to remove the "L" plates from the front and back of the car. What a wonderful feeling it was to think that I was no longer classed as a learner! I had passed my test, and was now regarded as a qualified driver.

Would you be upset if I told you that you were all learners? You are, for the word "disciple" means "learner", and whilst you are on the receiving end of Christian teaching and instruction in church, home and Sunday School, you are classed as disciples or learners.

The day came in the lives of the twelve disciples whom Jesus called to follow Him and learn of Him, when they were fit to go out in His name to preach, teach and convert. Jesus then gave them a new title—they were called "Apostles", and the word means "one who is sent forth". The disciples had passed *their* test, and were qualified to obey the Master's words: "Go ye, therefore, and teach all nations, baptizing them in the name of the Father, and of the Son, and of the Holy Ghost; teaching them to observe all things whatsoever I have commanded you; and, lo, I am with you alway, even unto the end of the world."

The day will come when Jesus will look into your heart and say, "This disciple of Mine is ready to be made an apostle"—the learner is ready to be sent forth. And if the call of Jesus comes to you to become a minister, or a missionary, or a Sunday School teacher, or a doctor, or a nurse, remember the response made by the child Samuel in the house of the Lord, "Speak; for Thy servant heareth"; and also the response made by the young man, Isaiah, in the temple at Jerusalem, "Here am I; send me".

You will never regret making such a decision, and God will bless you, and honour you through that decision.

PRAYER
AND A PATCHWORK QUILT

"God hath heard me; He hath attended to the voice of my prayer" Psalm 66. 19

THE members of a certain church were busy preparing for a sale of work, and as they arranged the various stalls, a parcel arrived as a gift for the sale. Inside was a patchwork quilt made by a very old lady. It was made of many brightly-coloured pieces of material. The ladies, arranging the sale, wondered where to place it. The patchwork quilt looked so old-fashioned and out of place alongside the other up-to-date things on display.

At last someone offered to display it, but when the sale was opened, many people smiled when they saw the old-fashioned quilt, and passed it by.

At last the day came to an end, and the minister was sorry to see the quilt still on the stall, for he knew the old lady well, and how much she loved the church, and also how much time she had put into the making of the patchwork quilt.

Just as the sale was closing, in walked a missionary who was to speak the following day at missionary services. Noticing the quilt he said, "That's just what I could do with". But the price was too high. When the old lady heard that the missionary was interested in her work, she said that he could have the quilt as a gift.

So the old lady's quilt found its way into the missionary's luggage, and eventually into the missionary's home in Africa.

One day the missionary's bedroom was being cleaned, and the quilt, along with other things, was hung out to air on the veranda. Just then the chief of a neighbouring village was passing by, and noticed the brightly-coloured quilt. Africans like bright colours, and so this chief asked the missionary if he could buy it. The missionary said that it was not for sale.

For a long time the missionary had wanted to buy a piece of land in this chief's village, so that a church could be built there, and Christian work commenced, but the chief had always refused his request.

This was the missionary's opportunity. He said to the chief, "For a long time now I have wanted a piece of land in your village to build a church. If you will give me the land, you can have the quilt in payment." The chief readily agreed. The land was given, the church was eventually built, and a fine piece of Christian work was commenced in that village.

Some time later the missionary sent a letter to the minister of the church that had supplied the patchwork quilt, asking him to pass on the good news to the old lady.

He did so, but was astonished to find that the old lady was not in the least surprised. She said, "I am glad to know the quilt has been used by God in this way, but I am not really surprised, for, you see, *every* patch on that quilt was put on with a prayer. God heard me, and attended to the voice of my prayer. I knew He would use it somehow, so why *should* I be surprised?"

"As o'er each continent and island
   The dawn leads on another day,
The voice of prayer is never silent,
   Nor dies the strain of praise away.

So be it, Lord; Thy throne shall never,
   Like earth's proud empires, pass away;
Thy Kingdom stands and grows for ever,
   Till all Thy creatures own Thy sway."

THE CHRIST OF THE ANDES

"Wisdom is better than weapons of war" Eccles. 9. 18

DURING the year 1900 there was talk of war between Chile and Argentina. These two neighbouring republics began to make huge preparations for battle. Heavy taxes were imposed, and munitions of war manufactured.

But at Eastertide of that year a certain Argentinian bishop named Benavente made a great appeal at Buenos Aires that war should be avoided and that the Spirit of Him, Who died for all mankind upon the cross of Calvary, should be allowed to mediate between the two nations.

His words made so great an impression upon his people that he was enabled to make a pilgrimage of peace up and down the land. Soon a Chilean bishop took up the challenge, and started a similar crusade amongst his people. Petitions were sent to the two Governments, and so strong was the desire for peace on the part of the people that they were compelled to suspend their preparations for war. After discussion together the Governments agreed to invite King Edward VII of Great Britain to arbitrate between them. The result was that an agreement was made, and a treaty, pleasing to both nations, was signed, and war was averted.

So great was the popular demand that some expression of gratitude for this should be made, that orders were given that the guns of both Argentina and Chile should be scrapped and that a huge bronze statue, representing Jesus Christ, should be cast from the metal. The statue was duly cast and was carried to the highest pass over the Andes, 14,000 feet above sea-level; and on March 13th, 1904, the ceremony of dedication took place. Amid scenes of great rejoicing, the Chilean and Argentinian people present passed over to each other's soil, and the statue was reverently unveiled. It is a life-size figure of Jesus Christ, with His feet resting upon the globe of the world, representing the prophecy that one day the kingdoms of this world will become part of the Kingdom of Christ, Who will then be Lord of lords and King of kings.

Inscribed on the base of the statue are these memorable words:

"Sooner shall these mountains crumble into dust than Argentines and Chileans break the peace to which they have pledged themselves at the feet of Christ the Redeemer."

On the opposite side of the pedestal are the words:

"PEACE ON EARTH, GOODWILL TO ALL MEN".

Now see what happened to some schoolboys about the same time.

In a certain town, on the border of the two countries, was a school attended by both Argentinian and Chilean boys, and the quarrel between the two countries caught fire among the boys of this school.

One night, when all was dark, a band of boys from Argentinian homes in the town went to the school-garden. The next morning every garden-plot belonging to the Chilean boys was discovered to be ruined.

The next night another band of boys made their way through the darkness to the school-garden, and next morning the plots belonging to the Argentinian boys were as bad as were those of the Chileans.

On Good Friday morning one of the young Argentinian ring-leaders sat in church, listening to Bishop Benavente. He heard the plea, made in the name of the crucified Lord of men, that peace should prevail. He grew very ashamed of the part he had played, and decided to respond to that appeal.

He shared his thoughts with the other boys, and such was the power of his leadership that for several nights the boys took rakes, shovels, spades, trowels, and worked long hours by moonlight to restore each garden-plot belonging to the Chilean boys—even to the point of re-planting them.

It was not long before the Chilean boys found out what was happening, and the same good spirit laid hold of them, and they, too, set to work; and by the time peace between the two nations had become finally established, and plans were made for the erection of the great statue of Jesus Christ—the CHRIST OF THE ANDES—the school-garden was again a joy to behold.

Christian boys and girls can do so much for world peace. Peace stands for order, beauty, love, brotherhood, understanding and co-operation. Will YOU live, pray and work for

"PEACE on earth, goodwill to ALL men".

NICKNAMES

"The disciples were called Christians first in Antioch"
Acts 11. 26

WHAT is a nickname? A name that "nicks"? It looks like that, and some nicknames are meant to hurt. A nickname is really an "eke-name", which means an extra name.

We have our family name (our surname)—we are born with that—and I belong to the large world family of "Jones". Then we have our Christian name, or names. Both of these names are registered for us, and confirmed at our dedication or baptism. And sometimes we have a nickname, given to us because it fits, or because we deserve it, or because in some way it describes us.

The Bible is full of nicknames. Esau called Jacob "the Supplanter". James and John were called "the sons of thunder" (they must have been very noisy at times!) and "Peter" is really a nickname Jesus gave to Simon when He called him "Cephas" (which means "a stone").

In history we have Ethelred "the Unready"; William "the Conqueror"; William "Rufus"; Charles "the Simple"; and Charles "the Fat".

There are nicknames that are titles of honour. They cannot be claimed—they are given because they are de-

served. Abraham was called "the friend of God". What a
splendid nickname! John was called "the disciple whom
Jesus loved". Our Lord Himself received one from the
Pharisees when they called Him "the Friend of sinners".
It was not meant as a compliment, but to dishonour
Him—but how glad we are to be able to sing:

> "While He lived on earth abased,
> 'Friend of sinners' was His name.
> Still He calls them brethren, friends,
> And to all their wants attends."

Nineteen hundred years ago, in Antioch, there was a
company of people who were different from everybody
else. Their lives were better. No one could help seeing it.
The people of Antioch were famous for their cleverness in
making nicknames. They had to find a name for these
folk. Somebody had a brilliant idea. These people were
always talking about Christ; their ambition was to follow
Him; their business was to preach Him. So someone
coined the word "Christ-ian"—a follower of Christ.

The word caught on, and, as we are told in the Acts of
the Apostles, "the disciples were first called Christians at
Antioch". A new word was made to fit a new life.

The disciples in the New Testament never called themselves "Christians". They called themselves "disciples"
or "believers". They left other people to call them
"Christians", and, because they *were* Christians in every
sense of the word, they were *called* "Christians".

That is how it should be with us. To call oneself a
Christian is not the same thing as *being* a Christian. It is
not for us to call ourselves Christians. We must leave
that to other people to give us that splendid nickname—
IF WE DESERVE AND ARE WORTHY OF IT.

We must follow Jesus Christ and live for Him, with
Christ in our hearts, and Christ in our thoughts, and
Christ in all we do and say, so that people cannot call us
anything else than Christians because we deserve it, even
as the disciples of old were first called "Christians" at
Antioch because they deserved it.

CLEOPATRA'S NEEDLE

"For God so loved the world, that He gave His only begotten
Son, that whosoever believeth in Him, should not perish, but
have everlasting life" St. John 3. 16

IN London on the Thames Embankment is something
very interesting. It is known as Cleopatra's Needle.

It is a huge monument of granite standing by the side
of the river Thames. Carved thirty-four centuries ago
from the red granite quarries of Syene, it has passed
through adventurous days and seen many strange things.
It stood erect in Egypt when the Children of Israel came
to settle there. Moses, who once lived at Heliopolis, must
often have gazed up at this pillar. Some thousand years
or so later, it was moved to Alexandria at the request of
Queen Cleopatra, whose name it now bears. Here it
survived two thousand years, and saw the fall of four
great empires.

In the year 1878 it was erected in London—all the
eighty-six-and-a-half feet of it, weighing a hundred and
eighty tons. You can imagine the tremendous task of
transporting this huge lump of stone, first across the
desert sand, and then across the ocean. In the Bay of
Biscay the ship, towing the raft which supported this
giant needle of rock, got into difficulties. A great storm
arose, and the sailors decided to cut away the rope between
their ship and the raft, and so saved their lives. When the
gale subsided the raft and "Needle" were rescued by a
Spanish ship.

Eventually it arrived in England. But now I am going
to tell you a most interesting thing. Beneath the famous
stone, out of sight to passers-by, is a hollow space, and
in it have been placed quite a variety of articles, such as
sealed jars containing a man's lounge suit, a lady's dress,
illustrated papers, children's toys, a razor, cigars, a
complete set of coins, a London directory and photographs of twelve beautiful women—oh yes, and a packet
of hair-pins! Last of all, before the hollow was sealed
up, they put in the most wonderful thing of all for people

in a thousand years or more to see—a copy of the Bible in four languages, and a certain verse of the Bible in two hundred and fifteen different languages. That verse is John 3: 16: "For God so loved the world, that He gave His only begotten Son, that whosoever believeth in Him should not perish but have everlasting life"—the most wonderful text in the Bible—the "Gospel in a Nutshell" as some people call it.

That text will never be old, never be old-fashioned, or out-of-date. There will never be a time when men, women and children will not be glad to hear, and know the truth of those words—not just a few chosen people, but the great, wide world of human beings—white men, black men, red men, yellow men, men from the Arctic snows, from the lands round the Equator, from North, South, East and West—the great Love of God is for all peoples in all ages.

Our task, in *this age*, is to show forth the love of God in our own hearts and lives to all the people we meet, wherever we go in God's world.

THE HOPE OF THE WORLD

"Hope in our Lord Jesus Christ" 1 Thess. 1. 3

I DARE say many of you have seen Harold Copping's beautiful picture entitled, "The Hope of the World". It is said that, when Mr. Copping first painted this picture, the faces of all the children were white. Then one night he had a dream about his picture. In his dream he went into his studio, only to find a stranger busy at work on his painting! "How dare you touch my picture," cried the artist. The stranger looked round with a calm, sad, and serious face, and replied: "How dare you use only a white colour, when you have all these other colours available. Do you not know that these children come from many lands, from many peoples, and cannot possibly all be white?"

Just then the artist awoke, and he felt the rebuke of the stranger—the stranger he knew to be none other than Jesus Himself. He set to work immediately, and painted the picture as we know it to-day. In the centre Jesus sits, with a kind and loving face, and around Him are gathered five children, representing the different races of the world. There is the fair-haired and fair-skinned girl of these Western lands, around whom Jesus has one of His arms. A dark-skinned Indian girl sits on His knee; while on the other side is a little South Sea Islander and a Chinese boy; and sitting on the ground, gazing up into His face, one of the coloured children from Africa. It looks such a happy little group, with the hills beyond, and the blue sea in the distance.

Why is it called "The Hope of the World"? Who is "The Hope of the World"? You answer, "Why the Man in the centre of the picture—Jesus." And why is He "The Hope of the World"? Because He is the Son of God, Who came to tell us of God our Father; because He loved us so much that He was ready to suffer, die and rise again for our sakes; also because He is what the picture shows so clearly—the Friend of children.

A number of years ago a young lady had a great desire to go out as a missionary to India to tell the children there about the best Friend they could ever have.

Everything was arranged for her to go, and then she became seriously ill. When she recovered, however, the doctors insisted that she must never go to a land like India. Instead she became a teacher in a village school. One day while driving alone in the country, she wrote two verses of a hymn on the back of an envelope. Afterwards she taught them to the children of the Sunday School at Blagdon, where her father was the Superintendent. One day, when, according to habit, he asked the children to choose a hymn, they called for this new one. Rather puzzled, he enquired as to who had written it, whereupon his youngest daughter casually replied, "Oh, Jemima wrote it".

It is a hymn which most children know and love:

> "I think, when I read that sweet story of old,
>   When Jesus was here among men,
> How He called little children, as lambs, to His fold;
>   I should like to have been with Him then."

Afterwards Mrs. Luke (as she became, on marrying Rev. Samuel Luke, the Congregational minister of Clifton, Bristol) added the third verse, which made it a missionary hymn:

> "But thousands and thousands who wander and fall,
>   Never heard of that Heavenly Home;
> I should like them to know there is room for them all,
>   And that Jesus has bid them to come."

So, although Mrs. Luke never became a missionary, she has inspired many another to go forth and tell of the love of Jesus.

Some time ago the picture "The Hope of the World" was shown on a screen, by a missionary in India, and to a little girl it was so real that she walked up to the sheet and said, "I want that Man to put His hand on *my* head".

That is what every child has felt on hearing about Jesus:

> "I wish that His hands had been placed on my head,
>   That His arms had been thrown around me,
> And that I might have seen His kind look when He said,
>   'Let the little ones come unto Me'."

You who know and love Jesus, can show by your lives, and through your prayers, that Jesus is still the best Friend.

> "I long for the joy of that glorious time—
>   The sweetest and brightest and best—
> When the dear little children of every clime
>   Shall crowd to His arms and be blest."

FORGIVE US...AS WE FORGIVE

"Peter said, 'Lord, how oft shall my brother sin against me, and I forgive him? Till seven times?' Jesus said, 'I say not unto thee, until seven times; but, until SEVENTY TIMES seven'"
St. Matt. 18. 21 and 22

A DELIGHTFUL story has been told illustrating the meaning of the above question asked by Peter, and the complete answer given by Jesus.

Two little children, who were twins, seven years of age —a boy named Dickie and a girl named Dorrie—lived at the seaside, but in rather an isolated spot. They were able to enjoy the beauty of the surrounding countryside, and also have a swim or splash around in the sea whenever they felt like it. They were very happy and contented until their older brother Jim came home from boarding-school for his holidays. Jim used to make their lives miserable by teasing them and wanting to play rough games with them. How glad the twins were when he went back to school!

As it was too far for them to attend the nearest Sunday School, Mother told them Bible stories on Sunday afternoons. One Sunday the story was that of Peter asking Jesus, "How often must I forgive my brother when he sins against me?" Dickie and Dorrie were "all ears" at this question. And when they heard our Lord's reply, "Unto SEVENTY TIMES seven," they both gasped with amazement.

Story time over, they rushed out into the garden to talk this all-important matter over together. Dorrie said, "I suppose we must forgive Jim seventy times seven."

Dickie had been doing some arithmetic. "Look," he said, "it's 490 times. What a lot of times!"

There was silence for a few minutes while they put their thinking caps on. Then Dorrie said, "I know what we'll do. We'll keep a book, and put in it every time we forgive him." "Yes," said Dickie, "and then when we reach 490, he'd better look out."

Having found a small book with some blank pages,

they proceeded to enter in a record of Jim's misdeeds, all his teasing, unkindness, and the rest. Against each record they wrote, "We forgive Jim. Dickie and Dorrie". Number 1, 2, 3, 4, 5, etc.

During his summer holiday, Jim went shooting with a new gun which his father had given him. The twins followed at a distance to see how he would get on with this new but rather dangerous toy. Jim happened to see a movement in a hedge, and probably thinking it was some bird, he fired. Immediately there was a shriek from Dickie, and a shout from Dorrie. Poor little Dickie had been shot. Jim, greatly put about and distressed, ran for his father, and together they carried the little chap home. There it was found that he had only been tumbled over by the force of the shot, for a little book had prevented the bullet from entering his little frame. In its covers the shot was found all flattened out, causing the pages to stick together.

Father pulled the pages carefully apart; and then, looking up in surprise, said, "Jim, this is all about you. Your name is on every page." He then called Dorrie who, through tears, explained what it was all about. Poor Jim! He did feel ashamed of himself. His parents gave him a serious talk about his behaviour towards the twins. And later on, Mother explained to the twins that seventy times seven meant, NOT 490, but that forgiveness should be shown at *all* times. There was to be no limit to the number of times of forgiveness.

Jim became a real nice big brother to the twins from that day, so all worked out well in the end.

But 490 seems a lot, doesn't it? And yet Jesus said that we must not stop to count the number of times we forgive, especially since we expect God our Father to forgive us the countless times *we* do wrong, either to Him or to others.

Jesus on the cross of Calvary prayed, "Father, forgive them for they know not what they do." And Stephen, the first Christian martyr, prayed, even as he was being stoned to death, "Lord, lay not this sin to their charge."

Whenever YOU pray the Lord's Prayer, remember the meaning of the words, "Forgive us our trespasses, as we forgive them that trespass against us."

SAY IT WITH FLOWERS

"Consider the lilies of the field, how they grow . . . Solomon in all his glory was not arrayed like one of these"
St. Matt. 6. 28, 29

YOU have probably seen these words on a florist's window, "Say it with flowers". You can understand that. But when you read on another florist's window "We Telegraph Flowers" I can well imagine your being puzzled and saying, "How do they send the flowers along the telegraph wires? I have never seen any going along!" "How do they send flowers to people living say in Canada, or America, or Australia?"

Very good questions indeed, and with a simple answer! The florist who takes the order sends a message either by telephone, telegram or cable, to another florist in the town or place where the people who are to receive the flowers live. It is *this* second florist who selects the flowers, and delivers them to the correct address. (There are about ten thousand florists all over the world who have joined this lovely scheme, in order to supply flowers for each other.)

I don't know who first thought of the idea, but a Boston florist, as far back as 1917, conceived the slogan, "Say it with flowers," and people have been saying it with flowers ever since!

A bunch of flowers means that we want to show certain people—old people, sick people, poor people, that we love them and care about them, and do not forget them. It can be a bunch of lovely roses or carnations, or, as I have seen, a tiny bunch of wild violets, or daisies, or even dandelions! It isn't the cost, or even the flowers themselves, but the thought and the love behind the gift.

Every Sunday from churches up and down the land,

flowers are taken to homes where little boys and girls, and grown-ups are sick; or to hospitals where there are lots of sick folk; or to old and lonely people. With the flowers from my own church a card is sent in each case, giving the name of the church, and this message: "These flowers from our Communion Table bring you the love and cheer of the church."

God sent us flowers because He wanted us to have more than food, or clothing, or houses in which to live. He wanted us to have wonderful beauty in our gardens, and hedgerows, and in our homes. He placed our first parents in a garden where everything was exquisitely beautiful, and He wants us to cultivate the taste for everything that is lovely and beautiful in His world.

On one occasion two brothers (grown-ups) had a quarrel. One of them sent an unkind letter to the other. The brother who received the letter did a very sensible thing —he took it along to his minister for his advice. "What would you recommend me to do?" he asked his minister. The young man was naturally annoyed with his brother, and his minister was afraid that he would write an unkind letter back again—and that would accomplish nothing. "Perhaps your brother is worried," the minister said, "or there may be some misunderstanding. When you reply, why not 'say it with flowers'?" This he did, and shortly afterwards, the quarrel or misunderstanding had been sorted out; all was forgiven, and they were the best of friends, as well as brothers, again.

> "There's not a tint that paints the rose,
>   Or decks the lily fair,
> Or streaks the humblest flower that grows,
>   But God has placed it there.
>
> Around, within, below, above,
>   His Providence extends;
> He everywhere displays His love,
>   And power, with mercy, blends."

Whenever you want to show gratitude; whenever you want to give a simple but loving present; remember you are always safe if you SAY IT WITH FLOWERS.

THE CONCEITED SPIDER

"The Lord is the strength of my life" Psalm 27. 1

DO you like spiders? Very few people do—not even "money" spiders! I want to share with you an old Danish fable concerning a young spider.

Once in an old barn, high up in the roof in a dark corner, there was born a spider. One fine day he tried to walk, and gaining strength, discovered that he could also spin fine threads. He amused himself spinning threads, and let them flow out like long feelers into the world below. At last, one day, he had a great adventure. He began a thread, and fastened its end to the beam, and then let himself go. Down, down he went, as if in a lift, until he suddenly stopped. He caught hold of something and found that he was on the top of the barn door, alone in a new world full of sunshine and flies—lots and lots of lovely flies just waiting to be invited into his web. So our young friend made fast the long thread that stretched up into the heights above, and from that point began to make his web.

It was a wonderful piece of work, for he was a skilled engineer and a born mathematician. Slowly but surely the web took shape. Last of all he ran a line up to a dark corner in which he had chosen to make his home. This was the telephone wire to tell him when someone had called, and was now entangled in the web. It had been a lot of hard work, and he was tired and hungry, and certainly much thinner. He felt proud of his first web.

Soon his telephone wire began to vibrate, for foolish, blundering flies, large and small, came flying into his web. Out came our young spider, and dined until he was well-fed and content—and the flies he couldn't devour he wrapped up ready for a meal the next day.

So life went well with him. He grew fat, and felt very pleased with himself. Now one day, as he inspected his web to see that all was well, he noticed a thread which went from the upper edge of the web right up into the heights of the roof. He looked to see if he could discover the end, but it was too dark. "I wonder what that thread is for? It doesn't seem to go anywhere. I think I can get on without it." So he reached up, and nipped it through, and immediately the web collapsed in wreck and ruin. That particular line didn't catch flies, but it held up his web, and without it his web just fell into a hopeless mess and tangle. What a very silly spider he was—all because he had become too conceited and self-confident, and had forgotten the importance of that special thread, down which he had come from the upper beam in the first place.

Some people are like that spider. They come into this world from God, and for a while they keep up their connection with God. A slender line of prayer joins their hearts to Him. Then they get on in this world, and think they have all they want, and because they are rich, stop praying. They stop worshipping. They break the connection with their Heavenly Father, and they find out, one day, at very great cost to themselves, that they have made a terrible mistake.

The line the spider broke was the strength of his web. The Bible says, "The LORD is the strength of My life." All the health and strength and wholesomeness of your life depend on the slender thread of prayer by which your heart reaches up to God. And God's Love and Mercy and Guidance become real to you, as they come down to you.

DON'T EVER BREAK, FOR ONE SINGLE DAY, THAT VITAL LINK OF PRAYER BETWEEN YOURSELF AND GOD.

> "Prayer is the soul's sincere desire,
>   Uttered or unexpressed;
> The motion of a hidden fire
>   That trembles in the breast.
>
> Prayer is the simplest form of speech
>   That infant lips can try;
> Prayer—the sublimest strains that reach
>   The Majesty on high.
>
> Prayer is the Christian's vital breath,
>   The Christian's native air,
> His watchword at the gates of death;
>   He enters heaven with prayer."

THE DOG THAT BROUGHT
TWO BLIND PEOPLE TO JESUS

"Blind leaders of the blind" St. Matt. 15. 14

I AM indebted to the Rev. Dr. Trevor Davies, of Richmond Hill Church, Bournemouth, for the following story.

What would you say if you saw an Alsatian dog slowly walking down the aisle of the church, just before the service began? In a large Baptist church in St. Louis in America, Dr. Davies saw this happen. Behind the dog followed a man and a woman holding the end of his lead. Both were blind. The dog had brought them to church, and it was this same dog that brought husband and wife to know, love and serve Jesus Christ.

One Sunday morning, the blind woman was out for a walk with the dog, when, without any warning, the dog led her into the large church. She received a warm welcome and much spiritual help. After this happy and helpful experience she continued to allow the dog to lead her there each Sunday. Then one memorable Sunday, in response to the minister's invitation, she gave her life to Jesus Christ, and later was baptized.

By now her husband had become interested, and he also began coming to church; but certain doubts in his mind held him back from making a similar decision.

In this particular Baptist church it is the custom at every service for an invitation to be given for unconverted friends to accept Jesus Christ as their own personal Saviour. When Dr. Davies preached, he was asked if he would be willing to do so, if not, one of the deacons would give the invitation for him. Dr. Davies was only too pleased to give the invitation in the name of the Lord Jesus Christ; and to his delight, amongst others who came forward to accept Christ as Saviour and acknowledge Him as Lord, was this blind man.

Just as any one of us may be used of God, that fine Alsatian dog was God's instrument in bringing to Himself those two dear people—a wife and her husband—despite their great physical handicap.

At the Communion Service held the following Sunday morning, when the blind man, along with others, was received into the membership of the church, at least 1,200 people were present and partook of the Sacrament.

Much more could be said about the church and the people—but I want you to remember the Alsatian dog who, under God, led two blind people to Jesus Christ and His church.

If a dog can do that—what about us? Have you ever invited a boy or a girl, or a grown-up, to come to your church, especially if you know they don't go to any other place of worship in the district? I'm sure there is room in your Sunday School for some of your playmates—but have you ever done anything about it? If not, why not do something between now and next Sunday? Do not only ask them to come, but go and call for them, and BRING THEM WITH YOU! By so doing, you will not only help someone to come to church, but also, perhaps, be used by God to bring them to know the Lord Jesus Christ —and that would be the most wonderful thing of all!

"There might be a wandering traveller,
  Who far on the wilds would roam
And lift up his eyes to the broken clouds
  And trust me to guide him home.

O Lord, I would shine in a child's best way,
  With gleaming of life and light;
And if any follow my humble walk,
  Then help *me* to *lead* them right."

THE LIGHTS OF THE CHURCH

"Let your light so shine before men" St. Matt. 5. 16

THIS story goes back over four hundred years and concerns some people who lived in Southern Germany.

A rich nobleman lived in a beautiful house with his four daughters. As he grew older he wondered what he could do to help the people of the village. The little church was old, and a new church was badly needed. So he decided to build a beautiful church far up on the hill. It was to be so beautiful that, as soon as people entered it, they would begin to worship God.

The building of the church was commenced, and the nobleman—and from time to time his daughters—watched the stones being placed in position. It was a slow and difficult task, because all the material had to be carried up from the valley below.

At last the stone-work was completed, the roof put on securely, and the workmen started on the church furnishings. There were beautiful wood carvings, lovely stained-glass windows, a marble pulpit of purest white, and a belfry with a bell to call the people from far and near to worship. One day, as they were admiring the excellent craftsmanship, the eldest daughter said, "Father, what about the lamps? Where are you going to place the lights? The church in the evenings will be dark without lights."

The nobleman said, "There will be no lamps hung in the church. Every person coming to worship will bring his or her own lamp. I will bring mine and you will bring yours, and everyone in the village who comes will bring a lamp. I have provided little bronze lamps for everyone, even the children, and everyone will be responsible for bringing a light." The daughter replied, "But, what if a person fails to bring a light, or, for that matter, does not come?" Her father said, "Then some part of God's House will be dark and desolate."

And so it was. Over the entrance was carved this sentence, "Some corner of God's House will be dark and desolate if EVERYONE does not come to worship Him."

Long years have passed since then, but the little bronze lamps have been handed down from parents to children, and then to their children, until even to-day, when the bell rings on Sunday evenings, the village people go either alone or together up the hill, each carrying his or her lamp. The church is now called "The House of Many Lamps", and is always filled with worshippers, for no one wants his or her corner to be dark and desolate.

I hardly need ask you the obvious question: "Is *your* church a 'Church of Many Lamps'? Is your place or your seat occupied every Sunday? As a Christian follower of Jesus do you make it your personal business to obey your Master's words, 'Let *your* light so shine before men that they may see your good works, and glorify your Father which is in Heaven'."

Grow to love your church, and all that the Church of Christ stands for, so that you just cannot stay away, your greatest delight being to be present in God's House, taking an active part in the worship, and thus being a true light and witness to someone around you in need of Jesus, and the fellowship of His Church.

MILK OR WATER

"Whatsoever thy hand findeth to do, do it with thy might"
Ecclesiastes 9. 10

HERE is a story about a king in India who wished to give a great feast to his subjects.

In addition to all the different kinds of food required for the banquet, the food minister learned that he would require a great quantity of milk—30,000 gallons at least! So he gave orders to all the milkmen in the land that they were to "give" a gallon of milk each. "Give", mind you—they were not to be paid for it!

A huge barrel was set up in the middle of the town (it must have looked like a small swimming pool—only a dry one) and at night, in the cool of the evening, the milkmen were to come with their contributions of milk. The older milkmen "groused" about this imperious demand. "Let the younger milkmen give the milk—they are stronger than we." The younger milkmen, on the other hand, said, "The old milkmen have escaped this sort of thing in the past, let *them* give the milk." But deep down they all wondered what would happen. An order was an order, and all had been told to give a gallon of milk each.

At night the first man came with his tin—not of milk, but of water. "Catch me," he said to himself, "catch me giving milk; let the next man give the milk, and nobody will know what I put in." The second man came with his tin saying, like the first, "Let the one who follows me give milk, no one will know that I gave water."

At long last the barrel was almost full. As the last man emptied his tin he said, "What fools these men have been; they have all put in milk. My gallon of water will not be noticed in so much milk." The following day the food minister visited the spot, looked into the barrel, and was filled with consternation to discover—not 30,000 gallons of milk, but 30,000 gallons of water! Not a single drop of milk had been given for the king's feast.

If everyone in this church to-day had said, "I will not go to church this morning, others will be there"—if everyone had said that—this House of God would have been empty.

How often mother says to Tommy, "Now, please clear away all those toys and muddles before tea," and Tommy says to himself, "Oh, I'll leave that for Johnny to do; he's good at clearing away." But Johnny does not clear the toys and muddles away—he in turn leaves them for Tommy to put in the toy cupboard—so in the end, they stay where they are. Johnny and Tommy are like the milkmen—the first left his part to the second, and the second left his to someone else, and so all failed.

Jesus, before His Ascension, said to His disciples, "Go ye into all the world and preach the Gospel". If James had said, "John can do the preaching"; and if John had said, "Peter is the best preacher, let *him* do the preaching"; and if Peter had said, "Well, it's time these other fellows did a little more"—what in the world would have happened? Well, just nothing! Jesus Christ's work would have been completely neglected, we would have had no New Testament, and the Christian Church would have died a very early death. It is quite certain we should not be meeting in this way to-day if that had been the case.

Have you ever seen the Wayside Pulpit with the letters "CH - - CH"? What is missing? The answer is obviously "UR"—"you are", and if you are missing from your church, and the worship of God's House, something will suffer—some work will be neglected, some task that only you can perform will be left undone. You have a great responsibility towards Jesus Christ, and to your fellow Christians. Do not fail, or let either Him or them down. You will always be sorry about those lost opportunities which can never be regained. So, be faithful, and do not grow weary in *well-doing*!

NEAREST TO EVERYTHING

"I was glad when they said unto me, 'Let us go into the house of the Lord'" Psalm 122. 1

DR. JOHN MACBEATH, in one of his books, describes a visit he made to a large city in America. At his hotel he found the notepaper very interesting. On the top half of the sheet was an outline map of the centre of the city, and at the heart of it a miniature picture of the hotel, with the motto underneath, "NEAREST TO EVERYTHING". The Post Office was marked, Railway Stations, Library, Public Stores, Theatres, and many other places of interest —BUT NOT ONE CHURCH! Yet, Dr. Macbeath knew that there were four or five central churches within a few minutes' walk of the hotel.

Can a city have EVERYTHING if it hasn't got a church? If we take the Church of Jesus Christ *out* of our lives, can we truthfully say that we have everything without it? Some people think only of food, comfort, clothes, friends, money, having a good time, spending each week-end (when fine) at the seaside or with business friends. But Jesus Christ, God's Own Son, said, "Seek ye FIRST the Kingdom of God, and His righteousness, and all these *things* shall be added unto you." The *things* are added— they do not come first.

A life without WORSHIP, without RELIGION, without Christian FAITH, HOPE and LOVE, is like having eyes without sight, and ears without hearing, for it is a form of life WITHOUT GOD IN IT.

When the world around seems very attractive, when you receive invitations to go here, there and everywhere on a Sunday (the Lord's Day—the Day for RE-CREATION, the Day of Resurrection), and when it takes a lot of effort to stand your ground as a young Christian, remember these words:

> "Lord, how delightful 'tis to see
> A whole assembly worship Thee;
> At once they sing, at once they pray,
> They hear of heaven and learn the way.
> *I have been there, and still would go,*
> 'Tis like a little Heaven below.
> Not all my pleasure or my play
> Shall tempt me to forget *this* day."

" I was glad when they said unto *me*, 'Let *us* go into the House of the Lord'."

L.M.S.

"The Lord is *my* Shepherd" Psalm 23. 1

I WANT to use the letters "L.M.S." in three ways:
1. Before the railways in Great Britain were nationalized, we always used to speak about the "L.N.E.R." (the London and North Eastern Railway), the "G.W.R." (the Great Western Railway), and the "L.M.S." (the London, Midland and Scottish Railway). Many people to-day still use the old initials, although you will not find them on the timetables, and certainly not on the approaches to the large stations. So you will still come across people who say I am going by "L.M.S.", whereas they really mean "L.M.R." (London, Midland Region, of British Railways).

2. Have you heard of the L.M.S. missionary society (The London Missionary Society)? David Livingstone was one of the early pioneer missionaries to go out to Africa with this Society, and Alfred Sadd was the missionary who defied the Japanese in the South Seas during the last war. He would not disgrace the Union Jack by walking over it, and in the end, picked it up and presented it to the Japanese commander! Alfred Sadd, along with other Christians, was later put to death. Yes, the initials "L.M.S." mean a great deal when it comes to a missionary society doing a vital work throughout the world.

3. The LORD is MY SHEPHERD—the most important "L.M.S." of all. When the Caledonian Railway became part of the London, Midland and Scottish Railway, all the railway men received new caps with the letters L.M.S. on them. Some children asked one of the porters, who was also a Sunday School teacher, what the letters stood for. He told them that they stood for London, Midland and Scottish, and then he said, "I'll tell you a better meaning than that. When I see these letters they always remind me of the Psalm—'The Lord's My Shepherd'." Then he told them that Jesus was indeed the Good Shepherd, Who loves and cares for ALL His

sheep and lambs—the grown-ups, and the boys and girls. What a wonderful thing it is when you can say, and mean, "The Lord *is* MY Shepherd," because you know Him, you love Him, and you desire to serve Him.

Here is a five-finger exercise which may help you. First, hold out your left hand. Which is nearest to you— your thumb or your little finger? In my case it is the thumb and I expect it is the same with you. Now place the index finger of your right hand on the little finger of your left and work in towards yourself saying, "The — Lord — Is — My — Shepherd". When you reach your index finger you should be on the word "MY", and the thumb will stand for "SHEPHERD". A little boy who went into hospital had learned this exercise. His doctor said afterwards to the boy's minister, "I wondered why he held on to his index finger and thumb before his operation, but now I understand that your five-finger exercise helped him immensely; he was still holding his finger and thumb when he 'came round' in the children's ward." Yes, this little boy put his faith and trust in Jesus Christ to the test, and went for his operation believing in "MY SHEPHERD". What a difference that makes!

A famous actor once recited the twenty-third Psalm before a large audience and was greeted with great applause. Addressing an elderly minister who sat in the front row he asked him if he would kindly repeat the same Psalm. The godly old preacher did not possess the richness of voice of the actor, but slowly and with feeling repeated, "The Lord is MY Shepherd, I shall not want. . . ." At the end complete silence reigned. The actor sensed the unmistakable difference in the rendering and, putting his arm round the old minister, he said to the people, "I know the *Psalm*, but our good friend here knows the *Shepherd*." That makes all the difference in the world. Let it be your experience too.

"The Lord's MY Shepherd, I'll not want;
He makes me down to lie
In pastures green; He leadeth me
The quiet waters by.

Goodness and mercy all my life
Shall surely follow me,
And in God's House for evermore
My dwelling-place shall be."

HIDDEN TREASURE

"The Kingdom of Heaven is like unto treasure hid in a field;
the which, when a man hath found, he hideth, and for joy
thereof goeth and selleth all that he hath, and buyeth that
field" St. Matthew 13. 44

IN a window at Lambeth Parish Church, in south-east
London, is to be found the picture of a dog—a pedlar's
dog. And near the church is a piece of land known as
"Pedlar's Acre". The story goes that, over four hundred
years ago, a pedlar, i.e., a man who sells laces, matches,
pins, etc.—anything small and cheap—and his dog were
crossing this open space when the dog suddenly began
scratching on the ground. The pedlar, for the want of
something better to do, sat down and watched him at
work. It was not very long until the dog uncovered an
old pot which was filled to the brim with hundreds of
gold coins.

You can imagine how surprised the pedlar was. He
quickly covered the pot with earth again, marked the
place with a small stick, and went off in search of the
owner of the land. It happened not to be very good land
and so the owner accepted the offer of the pedlar and
sold it to him for half-a-crown. The pedlar became not
only the new owner of the land, but also the legal owner
of the hidden treasure.

Near to this piece of waste land was the Lambeth
Parish Church, and as a thankoffering for his wonderful
find, the pedlar gave a sum of money to the church, and
a stained-glass window was later placed in the church in
commemoration of the gift.

This old story reminds us of some words of Jesus, "The

Kingdom of Heaven is like unto treasure hid in a field; the which, when a man hath found, he hideth, and for joy thereof goeth and selleth all that he hath, and buyeth that field." The story that Jesus told is very much like the story of the Pedlar's Acre, but there is one big difference—I hope you noticed it.

The pedlar bought his land and his treasure for half-a-crown. The man in our Lord's story SOLD ALL THAT HE HAD to buy the field. You cannot buy the most precious thing in all the world for half-a-crown. If we want the wonderful life that Jesus offers of becoming citizens of His glorious Kingdom, then we must be prepared to sacrifice everything for it—the surrendering of all that we have and are to Jesus Christ as our Saviour and Lord.

The treasure of the Kingdom of Heaven is the free gift of Jesus Christ to believing boys and girls and grown-ups through faith.

"Take my life, and let it be
Consecrated, Lord, to Thee;
Take my moments and my days,
Let them flow in ceaseless praise.

Take my silver and my gold,
Not a mite would I withhold;
Take my intellect, and use
Every power as Thou shalt choose.

Take my will, and make it Thine;
It shall be no longer mine;
Take my heart, it is Thine own;
It shall be Thy royal throne.

Take my love, my Lord, I pour
At Thy feet, its treasure-store;
Take myself, and I will be
Ever, only, *all* for Thee!"

GOD'S ADVERTISEMENTS

"Called to be saints" 1 Corinthians 1. 2

A FEW years ago, two children, named John and Peggie, were taken to London for the first time for a holiday.

One night, after dark, they were allowed to go and see all the "lights of London town". They were spell-bound when they saw all the various illuminations, and the big coloured advertisements that flashed on and off which gave one the impression of motion. They had never seen anything like it before.

The next day was Sunday, and in the afternoon they had the pleasure of visiting at the home of some relations, where they had tea. It was getting dark when they eventually left their relatives' house and crossed the heath with their mother on their way home. On the edge of the heath stood All Saints' Church, Blackheath, which was lit up for the evening service.

Through the coloured windows the light shone forth, revealing figures of red-robed and blue-robed saints—one with a ship, another with a small model of a church, a third with a lamb, a fourth with a gospel. Peggie stopped and gazed in wonder at all these pictures of men and women. "Oh, Mother," she said, "are these God's advertisements?" John laughed and said, "Of course not, they are only stained-glass windows."

Mother wisely added, "I think they *are* God's advertisements, Peggie; they are pictures of God's saints—men and women, and some of them children too, who lived beautiful lives because God's light was shining through them. So they showed the world what God is like—how good He is, and how loving. They were good advertisements because they would make other people want God too."

A Sunday School teacher once asked her class the question, "What is a saint?" A bright little girl replied, "Please, Miss, it's a man that the light shines through". Why did she put it that way? Well, because, like Peggie, she had visited a church with beautiful stained-glass windows showing the saints of God. The little girl in the Sunday School class had looked at these windows from INSIDE the church, and noticed that it was *through* the saints in the glass windows that the light shone into God's House. No wonder she said, "A saint is a man that the light shines through".

A saint is a person whom the light of Jesus Christ shines through to others. The apostles, Christian martyrs, missionaries, Christian preachers and teachers—all these and many more have become God's saints, God's advertisements, because the light of His love has shone through them to others in need. Jesus said, "I am the Light of the world," and then turning to His disciples He said a very wonderful thing to them and about them, "*You* are the light of the world. Let your light so SHINE before men that they may see your good works, and glorify your Father which is in Heaven."

Yet it isn't only great people who are saints. Anyone who truly loves and serves Jesus is a saint.

When the Apostle Paul wrote his letters to the various churches under his care, he usually began by addressing himself to "the saints which are at Ephesus" or "the saints in Christ Jesus which are at Philippi", and in calling the people "saints" he was thinking not only of the church leaders there, but of all the grown-ups, and the boys and girls as well.

You and I, if we truly belong to Jesus Christ, are "called to be saints", to let the light of the love of God, in Jesus Christ, shine through us to others.

> "Though sun or moon I cannot be
> To make the whole world bright,
> I'll find some little cheerless spot,
> And SHINE with all my might!"

FOOTPRINTS IN THE SNOW

"Jesus said, 'No man, having put his hand to the plough and looking back, is fit for the Kingdom of God'" St. Luke 9. 62

TWO boys were having a wonderful time in a country lane because of a heavy fall of snow. They threw snowballs at one another, made a huge snowman, and were wondering what to do next when one of them looked over a gate into a field. The field looked like a very large white table-cloth with not a mark to be seen on it anywhere. Turning to his chum, he said, "Let us see which of us can make the straightest path across the snow". This the other agreed to and so immediately both boys jumped the gate, and set off across the snow. One of the lads fixed his eyes on a tree on the opposite side of the field, and walked slowly towards it. The other boy started off that same way; got so far, then stopped and turned round to see how far he had come and what the line looked like, and then started off again. He did this a number of times. When both lads arrived at the other side of the field, they turned round to see how they had succeeded. One path was as straight as an arrow, while the other ran in a zigzag course. "How did you get your path so straight?" asked the boy with the zigzag lines. "Why," said his friend, "I kept my eyes on this tree, and didn't take them away until I reached the end of the field. You must have stopped and looked back, and wandered off your course." And so he had!

Jesus said the same thing about those who say they want to follow Him but who keep looking back on the old life, instead of constantly looking forward to the new life that Jesus offers. Remember the words in the Epistle to the Hebrews, "Let us run with patience the race that is set before us, looking unto JESUS, the author and finisher of our faith."

"Turn your eyes upon Jesus,
　Look full in His wonderful face;
And the things of earth will grow strangely dim
　In the light of His glory and grace."

MUTINY ON "THE BOUNTY"

"Thy word have I hid in mine heart, that I might not sin against Thee" Psalm 119. 11

IN the years 1788 and 1789, a British ship named "The Bounty" was anchored for some months off the island of Tahiti in the South Seas. The natives of the island were very kind to the British sailors, holding feasts for them. And when at last the Commander of the ship said that it was time to sail, some of the men objected— they had been spoiled by the lazy and comfortable life ashore. However, ship discipline must be firm, so eventually the ship sailed. But a number of the sailors rebelled against leaving Tahiti and rose in mutiny, turning the Commander and those men who were faithful to him adrift in a boat with some provisions, while they themselves returned in "The Bounty" to Tahiti. Among these mutineers was a man named John Adams, whose future we shall follow.

Mutiny is a very serious offence—a Commander on a ship is like a king on shore—so mutineers are liable to be severely punished. Some of the sailors who returned to Tahiti remained there but later on were arrested and brought to trial. John Adams and eight others had decided not to run this risk, and sailed off in "The Bounty" to find a safer refuge. They landed on a small island called Pitcairn Island. But there these men did not live happily together—they quarrelled and fought among themselves. In ten years so many terrible things had happened that John Adams was the only man left alive.

John Adams now found himself the only man on the desert island, with his native wife, the widows of the other men, and about twenty children. The ship, "The Bounty", had been eventually broken up, but among the things rescued were two books, and now with plenty of time to read and think John Adams began to study them. One was a Bible, the other, a Prayer Book.

In time John Adams came to see how wrong he had been—what a wicked life he had led! He poured out his soul to God in prayer, and asked forgiveness. Then things began to happen. He loved the children, and the children loved him, and he set himself to teach them all he knew.

The children proved to be good pupils. They learnt from him how to read and write and, as they grew up, he taught them, amongst other things, farming and carpentry and, best of all, he taught them about God. The Bible was the book upon which this large family grew in grace, and in the knowledge and love of God.

In 1814 (about fifteen years after John Adams had come to be the only man left on Pitcairn Island) a British ship landed there, and Adams, knowing that it was his duty to give himself up to the British crown, came bravely forward and surrendered to the ship's commander. The ship's officers were astonished to find such a company of young, English-speaking people—all polite, well-behaved and friendly. After hearing John Adams' story, and on learning all that was being accomplished on the island, the Commander felt that it would be going beyond the bounds of justice to have him arrested and taken back to England.

So the story, as you have heard it, was brought to Britain, and in the end the King granted John Adams a free pardon. The Union Jack now flies over Pitcairn Island, and the people are proud to belong to the British Commonwealth.

But what if there had been *no* Bible on that island? The story would have had a very different ending.

How essential, therefore, it is for everyone of us to read, and know the Word of God, and to be able to say with the Psalmist, "Thy word have I hid in mine heart, that I might not sin against Thee. I will delight myself in Thy statutes; I will *not* forget Thy word."